THE SKIN I'M IN

by
Sharon G. Flake

Student Packet

Written by
Marilyn Perlberg

Contains masters for:

2 Prereading Activities
4 Vocabulary Activities
1 Study Guide
2 Character Analysis Activities
3 Literary Analysis Activities
1 Writing Activity
3 Quizzes
1 Novel Test

PLUS   Detailed Answer Key
and Scoring Rubric

Note

The 2000 Jump at the Sun/Hyperion Paperbacks for Children edition of the novel, © 1998 by Sharon G. Flake, was used to prepare this guide. The page references may differ in other editions.
Novel ISBN: 0-7868-1307-5

Please note: This novel deals with sensitive, mature issues. Parts may contain profanity, sexual references, and/or descriptions of violence. Please assess the appropriateness of this book for the age level and maturity of your students prior to reading and discussing it with them.

ISBN-10: 1-58130-945-7
ISBN-13: 978-1-58130-945-4

To order, contact your local school supply store, or—
Novel Units, Inc.
P.O. Box 97
Bulverde, TX 78163-0097

Web site: www.novelunits.com

Lori Mammen, Editorial Director
Andrea M. Harris, Production Manager/Production Specialist
Taylor Henderson, Product Development Specialist
Heather M. Marnan, Product Development Specialist
Suzanne K. Mammen, Curriculum Specialist
Jill Reed, Product Development Specialist
Adrienne Speer, Production Specialist

Getting the "Lay of the Land"

Directions: Prepare for reading by answering the following short-answer questions.

1. Who is the author?

   _____

2. What does the title suggest to you about the book?

   _____

   _____

   _____

   _____

3. When was the book first copyrighted?

   _____

4. How many pages are there in the book?

   _____

5. Thumb through the book. Read three pages—one from near the beginning, one from near the middle, and one from near the end. What predictions can you make about the book?

   _____

   _____

   _____

   _____

   _____

6. What does the cover suggest to you about the book?

   _____

   _____

   _____

   _____

Name _____

Freewriting

Directions: To help you understand *The Skin I'm In*, think about the words listed below. Then write for three minutes about each one. Be ready to share your thoughts with classmates.

1. teasing

   _____

   _____

   _____

2. freedom

   _____

   _____

   _____

3. friendship

   _____

   _____

   _____

4. bullying

   _____

   _____

   _____

5. loss

   _____

   _____

   _____

6. self-respect

   _____

   _____

   _____

© Novel Units, Inc.

Word Map

freak (1)	amazon (1)	ricochet (2)	solitary (5)
yoga (9)	deodorant (12)	sensitive (12)	nappy (13)
reaction (19)	concoction (19)	blotch (19)	evaluate (21)
bonus (22)	negative (22)	chronicling (24)	maggots (26)

Directions: Choose eight words from the vocabulary list. Complete word maps for each word. Use each word in a sentence that helps to describe the magazine cut-out, drawing, or symbol you choose.

Synonyms	Magazine cut-out, drawing, or symbol that shows what the word means
_____	
_____	
_____	
_____	
_____	
_____	
_____	

Word

_____

Definition in your own words	Word used in a sentence
_____	_____
_____	_____
_____	_____
_____	_____

Name _____

potential (33)	corporation (36)	curriculum (36)	restriction (38)
invests (52)	lottery (52)	smirk (52)	indescribable (54)
apology (70)	expectations (70)	philosopher (72)	institution (74)

Directions: Fill in the blank with a word from the vocabulary list. Use the word or phrase in parentheses to help you complete each sentence.

1. Momma lifts the _____ when Maleeka has been punished enough. (limit that has been set)

2. Charlese complains about the _____ thing on her tray. (impossible to describe)

3. Other teachers want Miss Saunders to follow the _____. (established courses of study)

4. Maleeka doesn't want Momma to be put in some _____ because Daddy died. (place for people who need care)

5. A lot of people talk to Momma with a _____ because they think she's not entirely normal. (a kind of smile)

6. A school cannot be managed in the same way as a _____. (business organization)

7. A student in class is teased about talking like a _____. (wise thinker)

8. Maleeka says Momma never _____ because repairs are always needed. (spends to get more money in return)

9. Maleeka doesn't think the _____ offered by John-John is sincere. (request to be excused)

10. Momma buys tickets for the _____ so that she and Maleeka can live less poorly. (contest for which a drawing is held)

11. Maleeka needs the office job because she is bright and shouldn't waste her _____. (ability to achieve)

12. Miss Saunders has high _____ for her career in teaching. (hopes)

 © Novel Units, Inc.

Vocabulary Chart

clients (78)	executives (78)	competitors (78)	computers (80)
disrupting (81)	meditates (84)	laundromat (87)	hassling (91)
gutted (91)	detention (104)	persistent (109)	phase (109)

Directions: Write each vocabulary word in the left-hand column of the chart. Complete the chart by placing a check mark in the column that best describes your familiarity with each word. Working with a partner, find and read the line where each word appears in the story. Find the meaning of each word in the dictionary. Together with your partner, choose ten of the words checked in the last column. On a separate sheet of paper, use each of those words in a sentence.

Vocabulary Word	I Can Define	I Have Seen/Heard	New Word For Me

Name _____

Crossword Puzzle

rehearse (111)	enthused (113)	insights (113)	fantastic (113)
fidgeting (116)	undermind* (118)	credibility (118)	corporate (120)
convertible (130)	majesty (133)	cologne (134)	dashiki (134)
sizzling (142)	lotion (148)	expelled (149)	shoplifting (154)
switch (155)	lobby (157)	hunch (168)	spearmint (169)

*spelling in the novel

Directions: Select ten vocabulary words from above. Create a crossword puzzle answer key by filling in the grid below. Be sure to number the squares for each word. Blacken any spaces not used by the letters. Then, write clues to the crossword puzzle. Number the clues to match the numbers in the squares. The teacher will give each student a blank grid. Make a blank copy of your crossword puzzle for other students to answer. Exchange your clues with someone else and solve the blank puzzle s/he gives you. Check the completed puzzles with the answer keys.

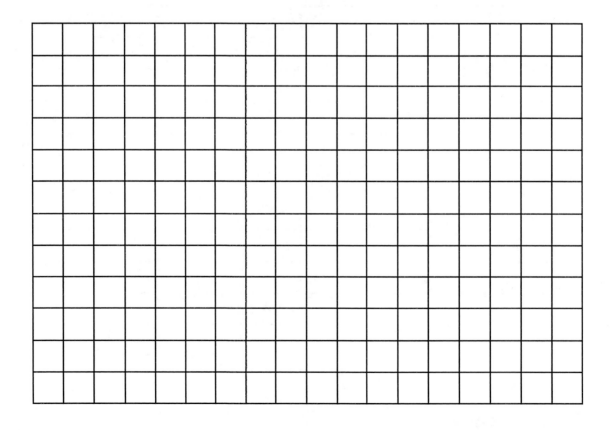

Name _____

Directions: Write a brief answer to each study question during or after reading each section. Use the questions to guide your reading and help you prepare for class discussion.

Chapters 1–3, pp. 1–15

1. In which grade level is Maleeka when the novel begins? How old is she? What is the name of her school?

2. Who is Miss Saunders? What does Maleeka think Miss Saunders will do?

3. What is unusual about Miss Saunders's face?

4. What does Miss Saunders say about Maleeka's skin?

5. What is the main idea of John-John's rap song?

6. What does Maleeka say about her grades in school?

7. What does Maleeka say about the clothes Momma makes for her? Why does Momma sew?

8. Who lends Maleeka clothes to wear at school? Why?

9. What does Tai teach? What is her relationship to Miss Saunders?

10. Which girls hang out daily with Maleeka in the school bathroom? What do the girls do?

11. Who is Caleb? What does Maleeka say Caleb liked about her?

12. Why doesn't Maleeka want to see Washington, D.C., again?

13. Why does Maleeka do homework for Charlese?

Chapters 4–6, pp. 16–32

1. What question is written on Miss Saunders's classroom blackboard?

2. How does Maleeka respond when Miss Saunders asks, "What's my face say?" Why does Maleeka respond that way?

3. How does Miss Saunders explain the blotch on her face?

4. What is Miss Saunders's purpose for being at McClenton?

5. How is Momma able to buy new clothes for Maleeka?

6. Why does Charlese want to be Maleeka's writing partner? What happens when Desda is picked to be Maleeka's partner?

7. Why can't Desda spend the scholarship money she won for her cooking?

8. Whom does Maleeka think she would have been centuries ago? How does she sign her fictional diary?

9. What does Miss Saunders say about the diary? What does Desda tell Miss Saunders about her contribution to the writing?

10. Who really kissed Daphne Robinson's boyfriend in the hall? What happens when Miss Saunders grabs Maleeka's hand?

Chapters 7–10, pp. 33–53

1. What do Miss Saunders and Momma agree upon as a result of the fight?

2. Is Momma pleased with Miss Saunders? Are the teachers pleased with Miss Saunders?

3. What is Maleeka's relationship to Sweets? What school does Sweets attend?

4. Does Sweets have better grades than Maleeka? What does Maleeka think it takes to enter Sweets's school?

5. Who gave Maleeka her pink hand mirror? What does the mirror help Maleeka remember about her skin color?

6. What does Maleeka expect people to do when she gets a new haircut?

7. Does everyone in Ronnie's shop like Maleeka's short haircut? Does Maleeka think she looks good?

8. Why does Maleeka go into the school bathroom and cry?

9. Does Momma make money on the stock market? Is Momma wealthy or poor?

10. Does Maleeka think Momma is smart or dumb? Why do friends tell Maleeka not to complain about Momma?

Chapters 11–13, pp. 54–74

1. What does Charlese find on her hamburger bun when she leaves the lunch line?

2. Why does Maleeka get back in the lunch line with Charlese's tray?

3. Which part of Charlese's lunch does Maleeka ask Miss Brown not to throw out?

4. Why does Maleeka grin when she leaves Charlese to sit with Desda?

5. Why isn't Maleeka in the same math class as Charlese and the twins?

6. What is important about the lie Maleeka tells Raise about Charlese's social studies paper?

7. How does Charlese punish Maleeka for not handing over the social studies paper?

8. Which book does Miss Saunders give Maleeka to read?

9. Who tells Maleeka she acts like she's too good for him?

10. What does Miss Saunders see on the blackboard?

11. Which play by Shakespeare does Miss Saunders discuss with the class?

12. According to Jerimey, whom should one love the most?

13. Why does Maleeka think no one should love too much?

Chapters 14–16, pp. 75–90

1. What did Miss Saunders do for a living before she came to McClenton?

2. What did Miss Saunders learn by checking Maleeka's records?

3. What does Miss Saunders want to do for a living now?

4. What is important about the conversation between Maleeka and Miss Saunders on the way to the office?

5. When Miss Benson says she hates pushy people, whom does she have in mind?

6. Why do parents call to complain? Whom do they complain about?

7. What does Akeelma make up her mind to be?

8. Why doesn't Momma want Maleeka to visit Charlese's place?

9. What is taking place when Maleeka visits Charlese?

10. Why can't Charlese get enough sleep?

11. How old is JuJu?

Chapters 17–19, pp. 91–110

1. Why does no one hear Maleeka yell when two boys assault her? Why do the boys let her go?

2. What does Maleeka do to comfort and express herself after the assault?

3. Where should Maleeka be instead of hanging out in the bathroom?

4. What does Charlese do with Maleeka's diary in the bathroom?

5. What is the only reason Charlese lets Maleeka hang out? When will Charlese abandon Maleeka?

6. Who breaks up the girls' bathroom meeting? Which of the girls is scolded the most and told to choose her friends better?

7. Why is Caleb in detention?

8. Whose name appears at the bottom of the last two diary letters in this section? What is the subject of these letters?

9. How does Caleb explain leaving Maleeka during the bus trip? Why does he want to be her friend again?

10. Does Maleeka trust and forgive Caleb?

Chapters 20–23, pp. 111–129

1. Why does Miss Saunders want to see Maleeka after school? Why is Maleeka late for the meeting?

2. Why is Miss Saunders in the auditorium? Who is with her?

3. What does Maleeka overhear that makes her stop in her tracks and stay to eavesdrop?

4. How does Miss Saunders feel about her students' insights? about their test-taking skills?

5. Does Tai agree that students should be held to standards? that tests are the only way to prove knowledge?

6. What does Tai say will ruin Miss Saunders at McClenton?

7. How does Miss Saunders discover Maleeka's presence in the auditorium?

8. Why doesn't Miss Saunders want her personal business known by students?

9. What does Maleeka decide to enter in the library contest?

10. How does Maleeka find out that Daddy was also a writer?

11. How does Daddy describe Maleeka in his poem about her?

12. Why does JuJu complain to Mr. Pajolli about Miss Saunders? Why doesn't JuJu complain about other teachers?

13. How long has Charlese been in the seventh grade?

Chapters 24–27, pp. 130–151

1. Why does Maleeka smile after John-John calls her "Midnight"?

2. What is the purpose of the get-together Caleb invites Maleeka to attend?

3. What is Caleb's opinion of the kind of friend Charlese is to Maleeka?

4. Why does Maleeka go along with Charlese's plan to get back at Miss Saunders?

5. Why does Miss Saunders leave her classroom door unlocked?

6. Why is Miss Saunders's classroom decorated with ribbons, curtains, and pillows?

7. Why does Maleeka feel she has to do something to help destroy the room?

8. What does Maleeka do with Miss Saunders's grade book?

9. Does Maleeka want to burn the pile of money? Why does she do it?

10. What else catches fire when Maleeka burns the money? Does she want that to happen?

11. Why is Maleeka the only girl seen by the janitor?

12. What is the cost of the school damage? What does Momma say about payment?

13. What does Maleeka want from Charlese in exchange for taking sole blame?

Chapters 28–32, pp. 152–171

1. Why do boys attack John-John? Who comes to John-John's rescue?

2. Why does Maleeka receive a letter from the library? What does she do with the letter?

3. Does Maleeka think Charlese's offer of $100 is enough? Why does Maleeka continue to hide Charlese's guilt?

4. Why does Miss Saunders pay a visit to Maleeka and Momma? How does Maleeka respond to Miss Saunders?

5. How does Maleeka get back in school after being suspended?

6. When does Maleeka reveal the guilt of Charlese and the twins? Who else is present at the time?

7. What happens to the twins and Charlese after Maleeka tells the truth?

8. Why does Mr. Pajolli release Maleeka from her school office job?

9. What does Maleeka receive from Caleb?

10. How does John-John greet Maleeka when she returns to class?

Metaphors and Similes

A **metaphor** is a comparison between two unlike objects. For example, "he was a human tree." A **simile** is a comparison between two unlike objects that uses the words *like* or *as*. For example, "the color of her eyes was like the cloudless sky."

Directions: Complete the chart below by listing metaphors and similes from the novel, as well as the page numbers on which they are found. Identify metaphors with an "M" and similes with an "S." Translate the comparisons in your own words, and then list the objects being compared.

Metaphors/Similes	Ideas/Objects Being Compared
1. Translation:	
2. Translation:	
3. Translation:	

Feelings

Directions: Complete the chart below. Choose events that best show evidence of change in Maleeka.

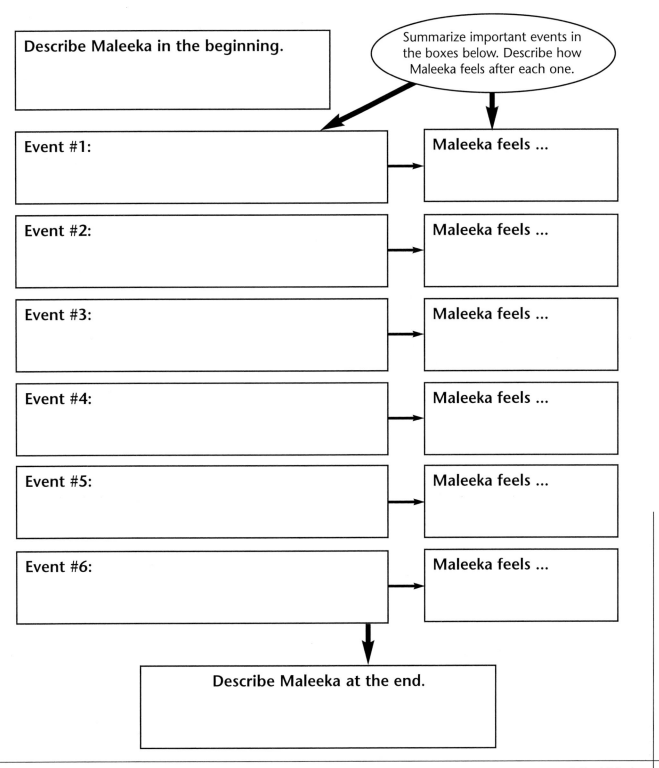

Describe Maleeka in the beginning.

Summarize important events in the boxes below. Describe how Maleeka feels after each one.

Event #1:

Maleeka feels ...

Event #2:

Maleeka feels ...

Event #3:

Maleeka feels ...

Event #4:

Maleeka feels ...

Event #5:

Maleeka feels ...

Event #6:

Maleeka feels ...

Describe Maleeka at the end.

Name _____

Sociogram

Directions: Write four of the following names in the circles: Miss Saunders, Charlese, Caleb, John-John, Momma, Sweets. On the "spokes" surrounding each character's name, write several adjectives that describe that character. Write a description of the relationship between Maleeka and each chosen character on the arrows joining them. Remember, relationships go both ways, so each line requires a descriptive word.

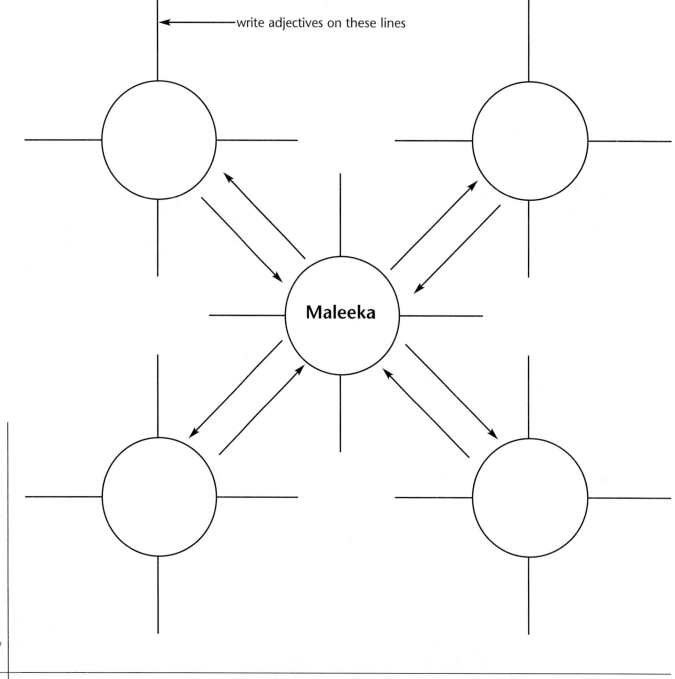

write adjectives on these lines

Maleeka

Name _____

Thematic Analysis

Directions: Choose a theme from the book to be the focus of your word web. Complete the web and then answer the question in each starred box.

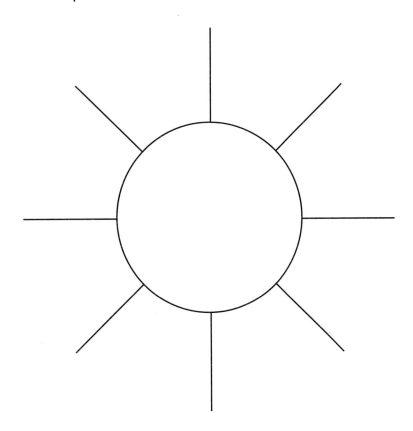

 What is the author's
main message?

 What did you learn
from the book?

Story Map

Characters_____

_____

Time and Place_____

_____

Problem_____

_____

_____

Goal_____

_____

_____

Beginning ⟶ Development ⟶ Outcome

_____

_____

_____

_____

Resolution_____

_____

_____

_____

Setting

↓

Problem

↓

Goal

↓

Episodes

↓

Resolution

Name _____

Directions: Explore the lives of people forced from their homes in Africa by slave trade in the southern United States before 1865. Research conditions on slave ships. Use the Internet and printed sources such as African/African-American slave narratives. Present your findings in a one-page essay.

_____

_____

_____

_____

_____

_____

_____

_____

_____

_____

_____

_____

_____

_____

_____

_____

_____

_____

Name _____

Directions: Choose the correct letter to answer questions 1–15. Not all names will be used. Several may be used more than once.

a. Maleeka	b. JuJu	c. Tai	d. Miss Saunders
e. Charlese	f. John-John	g. Caleb	h. Desda
i. Akeelma	j. Kinjari	k. Momma	l. Daphne Robinson
m. Mr. Pajolli	n. Daddy	o. Sweets	

A. Matching: Match the following descriptions to characters from *The Skin I'm In*.

_____ 1. sews as a way to recover from grief

_____ 2. fights Maleeka instead of Charlese for kissing Worm

_____ 3. attends a school across town for smart girls

_____ 4. sings a rap song about Maleeka's black skin

_____ 5. has a white blotch across her face

_____ 6. wins cooking contests but can't help Maleeka with her diary

_____ 7. brings clothes for Maleeka and hurts her with mean words

_____ 8. older sister who takes care of Charlese

B. Fill in the Blanks

9. Miss Saunders and _____, the math teacher, were college roommates.

10. Maleeka has a bad feeling about _____.

11. Teasing on the bus trip caused _____ to move away from Maleeka.

12. Maleeka stops the teasing by doing homework for _____, the toughest girl in school.

13. The hand mirror with the pink handle reminds Maleeka that she and _____ had the same skin color.

14. _____ doesn't want to see Maleeka waste her potential.

15. Classmates pick on _____ because of her hair, clothes, skin color, and good grades.

Name _____

A. True/False

_____ 1. Charlese angers the lunch lady by making a wisecrack about the hamburger.

_____ 2. Maleeka is happy to help Charlese by taking back the lunch tray.

_____ 3. Maleeka plays a trick on Charlese by smearing the yuck on the new hamburger.

_____ 4. Maleeka does Desda's math homework in the lunchroom.

_____ 5. Charlese brings no clothes because Maleeka didn't deliver the social studies homework.

_____ 6. Tai gives Maleeka *Life of a Slave Girl*.

_____ 7. John-John thinks Maleeka acts like she's better than he is.

_____ 8. Miss Saunders discusses Shakespeare's *King Lear* with the class.

_____ 9. Momma's relatives helped Maleeka when Daddy died.

_____ 10. Miss Saunders wishes she could return to the business world.

B. Fill in the Blanks: Choose names from the list to complete each statement.

Mr. Pajolli	Akeelma	Miss Saunders	John-John
Charlese	Maleeka	Caleb	

11. Miss Saunders knows that _____ passed the test for the school across town.

12. Parents call to complain that _____ assigns too much reading and homework.

13. _____ vows to be strong.

14. Maleeka feels sorry for _____ when she visits her place.

15. Maleeka wonders if she can forgive _____ for his behavior on the bus.

Name _____

A. Multiple Choice: Select the best answer for each of the items below.

_____ 1. Tai believes tests are
   a. the only way to prove students know something
   b. the wrong way to prove students know something
   c. only one of the ways to prove students know something
   d. better than other ways to prove students know something

_____ 2. Miss Saunders and Tai agree that the seventh graders
   a. show little potential in Miss Saunders's class
   b. show little enthusiasm for Miss Saunders's class
   c. come up with great ideas in Miss Saunders's class
   d. should learn to like Shakespeare in Miss Saunders's class

_____ 3. Talking to Tai helps Miss Saunders understand that
   a. she's not a very good teacher
   b. the students have started to like her face
   c. she has too many family pictures on her desk
   d. her need to be perfect will ruin her at McClenton

_____ 4. Maleeka learns from Momma that
   a. Daddy once won a library writing contest
   b. Daddy earned his living as a professional writer
   c. Daddy saved photos of Maleeka in a plastic bag
   d. Daddy wrote a poem about his beautiful Maleeka

_____ 5. JuJu complains to Mr. Pajolli that
   a. Maleeka does homework for Charlese
   b. Miss Saunders lets Charlese cut class too much
   c. the teachers are giving Charlese too many Ds this year
   d. Miss Saunders is wrongly giving bad grades to Charlese

B. True/False

_____ 6. Charlese rips a hole in Miss Saunders's convertible.

_____ 7. Maleeka tells Charlese about the conversation in the auditorium.

_____ 8. John-John's teasing causes Maleeka to think of a poem about midnight.

_____ 9. Charlese and Maleeka want to help Caleb improve McClenton.

22 © Novel Units, Inc.

Name _____

_____ 10. Maleeka goes along with Charlese's plan because she is too scared not to.

_____ 11. Maleeka willingly sets fire to Miss Saunders's classroom.

_____ 12. The janitor spots Maleeka because she's the slowest to run away.

_____ 13. Miss Jackson phones to tell Momma about the damage at school.

_____ 14. The library letter informs Maleeka that she owes fines for overdue books.

_____ 15. Maleeka reveals that Charlese, Raina, and Raise damaged the classroom.

Name _____

A. Identification: Identify each of the following and explain its importance in the novel.

1. dark skin color

   _____

   _____

2. clothes sewn by hand

   _____

   _____

3. bus trip to Washington, D.C.

   _____

   _____

4. Akeelma letters

   _____

   _____

5. hand mirror with a pink handle

   _____

   _____

6. school across town for smart girls

   _____

   _____

7. lunch tray

   _____

   _____

8. poem found in a box inside a closet

   _____

   _____

9. foreign money on a table

   _____

   _____

10. watch slipped into a locker

    _____

    _____

B. Multiple Choice: Select the best answer for each of the items below.

_____ 11. John-John teases Maleeka although he
     a. likes her
     b. is jealous of Caleb
     c. is small for his age
     d. has the same skin color as she

_____ 12. Maleeka wears homemade clothes because Momma
     a. buys her used clothes
     b. plays the stock market
     c. deals with her grief by sewing
     d. wants her to wear hand-me-downs

_____ 13. Charlese gets her way with Maleeka by
     a. persuasion
     b. being a true friend
     c. bullying and threats
     d. bringing old clothes for Maleeka to wear

_____ 14. Maleeka remembers Daddy's advice to
     a. take care of Momma
     b. see herself as others see her
     c. look in the mirror and cheer up
     d. see herself through her own eyes

_____ 15. Maleeka realizes that she will get teased
     a. no matter how she looks
     b. until she gets a new haircut
     c. because she likes Miss Saunders
     d. unless she gets John-John to like Caleb

_____ 16. Miss Saunders sets an example for Maleeka of
     a. self-confidence
     b. how to grade papers
     c. proper office behavior
     d. getting along with Charlese

_____ 17. Maleeka writes diary letters that help her understand her
     a. dislike of writing
     b. dislike of history
     c. enslaving relationship with Charlese
     d. romantic relationship with John-John

____ 18. True friendship is most seen in Maleeka's relationship with
     a. Charlese
     b. Momma
     c. Raina
     d. Sweets

____ 19. The ending of the novel shows that Maleeka had to
     a. forgive Momma
     b. learn to accept who she is
     c. make peace with Mr. Pajolli
     d. learn to like doing homework

C. Essay: Choose two of the following to answer in well-developed essays on a separate sheet of paper.

a. Think about Sweets's comment on page 40: "It's how you feel about who you are that counts." Write an essay of three paragraphs telling how you feel about this idea. Use examples from the novel and from your own or another's experience.

b. Write a letter to the school board requesting the development of a program to solve the problem of bullying in schools. Use information from the book to argue your case. Be sure to include your own opinions about how to solve the problem.

c. Imagine that the novel doesn't end on page 171. Write a follow-up scene. Think about what might follow in Maleeka's life. How will Maleeka fit in at school? How will she get along with John-John, Miss Saunders, and Caleb? How will Maleeka deal with the problem of clothes now that Charlese is gone? Include your opinion whether or not Maleeka will decide to become a professional writer.

Answer Key

Activity #1: 1. Sharon G. Flake 2. Answers will vary. 3. 1998 4. 171 5. Answers will vary. 6. Answers will vary.

Activities #2–#3: Answers will vary.

Activity #4: 1. restriction 2. indescribable 3. curriculum 4. institution 5. smirk 6. corporation 7. philosopher 8. invests 9. apology 10. lottery 11. potential 12. expectations

Activities #5–#6: Answers will vary.

Study Guide

Chapters 1–3: 1. seventh; 13; McClenton Middle School (pp. 2–4) 2. the new English teacher; ruin her efforts to fit in, mess things up (pp. 2, 5, 7) 3. the white stain halfway across (p. 1) 4. It's pretty, like a blue-black sky after rain (p. 3). 5. Maleeka's so black she can't be seen (p. 3). 6. They're good, mostly As (pp. 4–5, 13–14). 7. They're homemade rags, a shame, bad-looking; to ease the pain of Daddy's death (pp. 4, 9, 12) 8. Charlese; Answers will vary (p. 4). 9. math; old college roommates (p. 9) 10. Charlese, Raina, Raise; talk, smoke; Maleeka changes clothes (p. 12). 11. Maleeka's former boyfriend; her eyes and cocoa brown skin (p. 13) 12. Everyone on the bus teased her; Caleb left her (pp. 13–14). 13. to get protection from teasing (pp. 14–15)

Chapters 4–6: 1. What does your face say to the world? (p. 16) 2. It says you're a freak; Miss Saunders embarrassed her twice (p. 18). 3. She was born that way; nothing worked to get rid of it (p. 19). 4. to figure out if she wants a teaching career (p. 21) 5. She got a bonus at work (p. 22). 6. She figures Maleeka will do all the work; Charlese walks out (p. 23). 7. She has trouble reading, so she won't be going to college (p. 23). 8. a slave girl; Akeelma (pp. 25, 27) 9. It's the best, most thoughtful piece so far; she had nothing to do with it (pp. 27–28). 10. Charlese; Daphne hits Maleeka in the face (pp. 29–31).

Chapters 7–10: 1. to have Maleeka work in the school office for no pay (p. 33) 2. yes; no (pp. 34, 36) 3. best friends; the school for smart girls across town (p. 39) 4. no; tan skin color and attitude (pp. 39–40) 5. Daddy; It's the same as Daddy's (pp. 40–41). 6. see and treat her differently (pp. 42–43) 7. yes; yes (pp. 44–45, 48) 8. Schoolmates tease her about her haircut (pp. 47–49). 9. no; poor (p. 52) 10. smart; Momma has the biggest heart of anyone in the neighborhood (pp. 52–53).

Chapters 11–13: 1. something indescribable that may have lived (p. 54) 2. Charlese orders her to do it (pp. 55–56). 3. the hamburger bun with the indescribable stuff on top (p. 56) 4. Charlese doesn't know she's eating the indescribable stuff Maleeka smeared on the hamburger (pp. 56–57). 5. Their class is for kids who know nothing about math (p. 60). 6. It's the first time Maleeka doesn't give Charlese what she asked for (p. 60). 7. no clothes to wear next day (p. 61) 8. *Life of a Slave Girl* (p. 62) 9. John-John (pp. 64–65) 10. a woman's face with one side cracked and drooping; the words, "the teacher with two faces" (p. 68) 11. *Romeo and Juliet* (pp. 69–70) 12. oneself (pp. 71–72) 13. Momma fell apart when Daddy died (p. 73).

Chapters 14–16: 1. worked for an ad agency (p. 76) 2. Maleeka passed the test last year for Central Middle School across town (p. 77). 3. teach (p. 79) 4. Maleeka feels it's the first time they're together without things falling apart (p. 79). 5. Miss Saunders (p. 80) 6. too much homework and reading; Miss Saunders (pp. 80–81) 7. strong (p. 86) 8. JuJu lets Charlese do anything she wants and run wild (p. 86). 9. a party that's gone on since the previous night (p. 87) 10. JuJu yells at her to help at the party (pp. 88–89). 11. 25 (p. 89)

Chapters 17–19: 1. The block is vacant; She fights back, digs in her fingernails, and bites (pp. 91–94). 2. write in her Akeelma diary (pp. 96–97) 3. working in the school office (pp. 98–99) 4. sets a page on fire with her cigarette lighter (p. 100) 5. to get her grades up; after the social studies book report is finished (pp. 100–101) 6. Miss Saunders; Maleeka (pp. 101–103) 7. Mr. Pajolli put him there for cleaning the boys' bathroom (pp. 105–106). 8. Maleeka's; forgiving Caleb (pp. 107–109) 9. He thought the teasing would stop if he left her; things still go badly for her and he likes her a lot (pp. 109–110). 10. no (p. 110)

Chapters 20–23: 1. to go over Maleeka's diary; She resents being put in detention (p. 111). 2. to check equipment for class speeches the next day; Tai (pp. 111–112) 3. Miss Saunders is flunking half her seventh graders this semester (p. 112). 4. fantastic, right on target; just terrible (p. 113) 5. yes; no (p. 113) 6. her need to be perfect (p. 115) 7. She sees Maleeka's reflection when she takes out a mirror to redo her lipstick (p. 115). 8. It can undermine her credibility (p. 118). 9. her Akeelma diary letters (p. 122) 10. Momma mentions it when Maleeka tells her about Akeelma (p. 123). 11. as brown, beautiful, brilliant (p. 124) 12. Miss Saunders is failing Charlese; Other teachers are giving Charlese the grades needed to move up (pp. 127–129). 13. This is her third year (p. 128).

Chapters 24–27: 1. She remembers a poem about the beauty and majesty of midnight (p. 133). 2. to discuss ways of improving McClenton (p. 135) 3. the kind who will get Maleeka locked up or shot up (p. 136) 4. She's scared of Charlese and too frightened to think of an excuse for not showing up (p. 137). 5. She believes the students should take responsibility for their school (p. 138). 6. The class will begin reading *Ali Baba and the Forty Thieves* (p. 138). 7. She doesn't want the others to think she's chicken (p. 140). 8. changes Ds to As (p. 140) 9. no; Charlese squeezes her shoulder hard and threatens her (pp. 140–142). 10. the curtains; no (p. 142) 11. She's the last girl to run, and the clothes keep falling out of the bag (pp. 142–143). 12. $2,000; Maleeka must pay (p. 148). 13. money to help pay for the damage (p. 150)

Chapters 28–32: 1. He got one boy busted for shoplifting; Maleeka (pp. 153–155) 2. She won the writing contest; hangs it on the wall next to Daddy's poem (pp. 157, 159) 3. no; Charlese put Miss Saunders's watch in Maleeka's locker, and it was found there (pp. 160–161). 4. to show the watch and get the truth about who is guilty; Maleeka won't tell (pp. 162–164). 5. Miss Saunders arranges it (p. 165). 6. when she returns to school and goes to Miss Saunders's classroom; Miss Saunders and Charlese (pp. 165–167) 7. The twins get suspended; JuJu sends Charlese to live with her grandparents in Alabama (p. 168). 8. He rewards her for telling the truth about Charlese (p. 168). 9. a sweet poem (pp. 168–169) 10. He says, "welcome back" (p. 171).

Note: Answers for Activities #7–#12 will vary. Suggested answers are provided where applicable.

Activity #7: Metaphor: "Miss Saunders is a motion machine this morning" (p. 67). Simile: "Skin dry and ashy like tree bark ate away by the desert wind" (p. 26).

Activity #8: Maleeka is 13 years old and in the seventh grade, teased for being dark-skinned and poorly dressed, but a very bright student trying to fit in at school (pp. 1–2, 4–5). Event #1: John-John sings a rap song about Maleeka being "so black" she can't be seen; Feeling: Maleeka wishes the building would collapse on top of her (p. 3). Event #2: Charlese criticizes Maleeka's appearance and blows smoke in her face; Feeling: Maleeka feels hurt and disrespected, as if slapped (pp. 12–15). Event #3: Maleeka proudly struts into school with a new hairdo, but her classmates tease her; Feeling: Maleeka is hurt, but thinking about Daddy seems to help her regain her confidence (pp. 47–49). Event #4: Caleb warns Maleeka that Charlese is trouble; Feeling: Maleeka is frightened of Charlese's plan, but more frightened of refusing to be a part of it (pp. 135–137). Event #5: Charlese intimidates Maleeka in to setting a fire in Miss Saunders's classroom; Feeling: Maleeka feels frightened, and feels a sense of injustice being done toward Miss Saunders and herself (pp. 141–142). Event #6: Maleeka tries to decide how to tell Charlese that she is planning on revealing that Charlese and the twins were involved in the vandalism; Feeling: Maleeka is terrified, but resolute about telling the whole truth (pp. 159–160). At the end, Maleeka is confident and in control of her actions. She misses her office job, but is excited and happy about her rekindled relationship with Caleb (pp. 168–170).

Activity #9: Adjectives—Maleeka: victimized, unsure, intelligent, angry; Miss Saunders: confident, hardworking, caring, tough; Charlese: cruel, self-centered, angry, violent; Caleb: concerned, caring, optimistic, handsome; John-John: immature, hurt, unkind, clownish; Momma: hopeful, loving, confused, hardworking; Sweets: confident, optimistic, intelligent, honest; Relationships—Maleeka to Miss Saunders: mistrusting; Miss Saunders to Maleeka: helpful; Maleeka to Charlese: fearful; Charlese to Maleeka: enslaving; Maleeka to Caleb: wary; Caleb to Maleeka: loving; Maleeka to John-John: avoiding; John-John to Maleeka: resentful; Maleeka to Momma: caring; Momma to Maleeka: maternal; Maleeka to Sweets: admiring; Sweets to Maleeka: friendly

Activity #10: Theme: discrimination (pp. 3–4); Author's main message: Skin color doesn't matter, but how you feel about yourself does matter. Lessons learned from the book: Our differences are what make us beautiful; One must feel beautiful to be perceived as beautiful.

Activity #11: Characters: Maleeka, Miss Saunders, Charlese, Caleb, John-John, Momma, Sweets; Time and Place: McClenton Middle School and neighborhood, present day; Problem: Maleeka has low self-esteem; Goal: Maleeka wants her classmates to stop teasing her and Charlese to stop bullying her; Beginning: Maleeka is teased for her dark skin and handmade clothing, and she accepts Charlese's bullying as a form of friendship; Development: Charlese pressures Maleeka into vandalizing Miss Saunders's classroom; Outcome: Maleeka confesses that Charlese and the twins instigated the vandalism. Resolution: Maleeka accepts her punishment and feels more confident, with Charlese moving and her love life improving.

Activity #12: Answers will vary.

Quiz #1: A. 1. k (pp. 8–9) 2. l (pp. 29–31) 3. o (p. 39) 4. f (p. 3) 5. d (p. 1) 6. h (pp. 23–28) 7. e (p. 4, throughout) 8. b (p. 8) **B.** 9. c (p. 9) 10. d (p. 1) 11. g (p. 14) 12. e (pp. 14–15) 13. n (p. 41) 14. d (p. 33) 15. a (pp. 4, 47)

Quiz #2: A. 1. T (p. 54) 2. F (pp. 55–56) 3. T (p. 57) 4. T (p. 58) 5. T (p. 61) 6. F (pp. 61–62) 7. T (p. 64) 8. F (pp. 69–74) 9. F (p. 74) 10. F (p. 79) **B.** 11. Maleeka (p. 77) 12. Miss Saunders (p. 81) 13. Akeelma (p. 86) 14. Charlese (p. 89) 15. Caleb (p. 109)

Quiz #3: A. 1. c (p. 113) 2. c (p. 113) 3. d (p. 115) 4. d (p. 123) 5. d (pp. 127–128) **B.** 6. F (p. 130) 7. F (p. 131) 8. T (pp. 132–133) 9. F (p. 135) 10. T (pp. 136–137) 11. F (pp. 140–142) 12. T (pp. 142–143) 13. F (pp. 145–146) 14. F (p. 157) 15. T (p. 167)

Novel Test: A. 1. Maleeka gets teased because of her dark skin color. At the end of the novel she learns to accept the skin she's in (pp. 3–5, 167). 2. Maleeka is ashamed of the clothes Momma sews. She can't say anything because sewing is Momma's way to cope with the loss of Daddy (pp. 8–9). 3. Teasing is so bad on the bus that Caleb moves away from Maleeka. The teasing gets worse after that, and Maleeka turns to Charlese for protection (pp. 13–15). 4. Maleeka creates diary letters of a slave girl named Akeelma. The letters win praise from Miss Saunders and first prize in a library writing contest (pp. 25–27, 157). 5. Maleeka finds the hand mirror Daddy gave her. The mirror helps her remember that she is his skin color and she looks nice (pp. 40–42). 6. Maleeka has the grades to attend the school but thinks it's for tan-skinned girls. Her friend Sweets attends and says it's not skin color that counts but attitude—knowing who you are (pp. 39–40). 7. Charlese orders Maleeka to get an exchange of food from the lunch lady. Maleeka tricks Charlese into eating the same yuck she had before (pp. 55–57). 8. Maleeka finds a poem Daddy wrote about her. The poem tells her she is brown, beautiful, and brilliant (pp. 123–124). 9. Charlese forces Maleeka to help destroy Miss Saunders's classroom by burning the money. The curtains accidentally catch fire (pp. 140–142). 10. Charlese slips Miss Saunders's watch into Maleeka's locker. Charlese thinks this will force Maleeka not to squeal about the other girls' guilt (p. 161).

B. 11. d (p. 4) 12. c (pp. 8–9) 13. c (throughout) 14. d (p. 49) 15. a (p. 48) 16. a (throughout) 17. c (throughout) 18. d (throughout) 19. b (Chapter 32)

C. Answers will vary. Refer to the scoring rubric on page 31 of this guide.

Linking Novel Units® Student Packets to National and State Reading Assessments

During the past several years, an increasing number of students have faced some form of state-mandated competency testing in reading. Many states now administer state-developed assessments to measure the skills and knowledge emphasized in their particular reading curriculum. This Novel Units® guide includes open-ended comprehension questions that correlate with state-mandated reading assessments. The rubric below provides important information for evaluating responses to open-ended comprehension questions. Teachers may also use scoring rubrics provided for their own state's competency test.

Scoring Rubric for Open-Ended Items

3-Exemplary	Thorough, complete ideas/information Clear organization throughout Logical reasoning/conclusions Thorough understanding of reading task Accurate, complete response
2-Sufficient	Many relevant ideas/pieces of information Clear organization throughout most of response Minor problems in logical reasoning/conclusions General understanding of reading task Generally accurate and complete response
1-Partially Sufficient	Minimally relevant ideas/information Obvious gaps in organization Obvious problems in logical reasoning/conclusions Minimal understanding of reading task Inaccuracies/incomplete response
0-Insufficient	Irrelevant ideas/information No coherent organization Major problems in logical reasoning/conclusions Little or no understanding of reading task Generally inaccurate/incomplete response

Notes